GUESS HOW MUCH
I LOVE YOU
Activity Sticker Book

Use the stickers from the back of your book
to complete the scenes on every page.

Written by
Sam McBratney

Illustrated by
Anita Jeram

WALKER BOOKS
AND SUBSIDIARIES
LONDON · BOSTON · SYDNEY · AUCKLAND

Little Nutbrown Hare and
Big Nutbrown Hare love the spring,
when things start growing after winter.

Ribbit, ribbit!

See if you can match some
stickers to the sounds.

Tweet, tweet!

Pitter-patter!

Buzz, buzz!

Squeak, squeak!

What will these hatch into or grow up to be?

eggs ——————————→ birds

caterpillars ——————————→ butterflies

tadpoles ——————————→ frogs

Little Nutbrown Hare —→ Big Nutbrown Hare

How many of these colours can you spot?

Blue   Red   Yellow   Green   Brown

On a summer's day there are colours everywhere.

Make a colourful place for
Little Nutbrown Hare to play.
Where is he hiding?

Can you hop as high as Little Nutbrown Hare?
What other actions can he do?

hopping

stretching

standing

sitting

blowing

running

smelling

Sometimes it is windy
in the autumn.

Add lots of leaves for
Little Nutbrown Hare to chase!

Little Nutbrown Hare is learning to count.
Count along with him.

One flying bird

Two munching mice

Three jumping frogs

Four tweeting birds

Five hovering dragonflies

Six fluttering butterflies

Seven slithering snails

Eight buzzing bees

Nine wriggling
caterpillars

Ten crawling ladybirds

Brrr… It is cold in the snow. But so much fun!